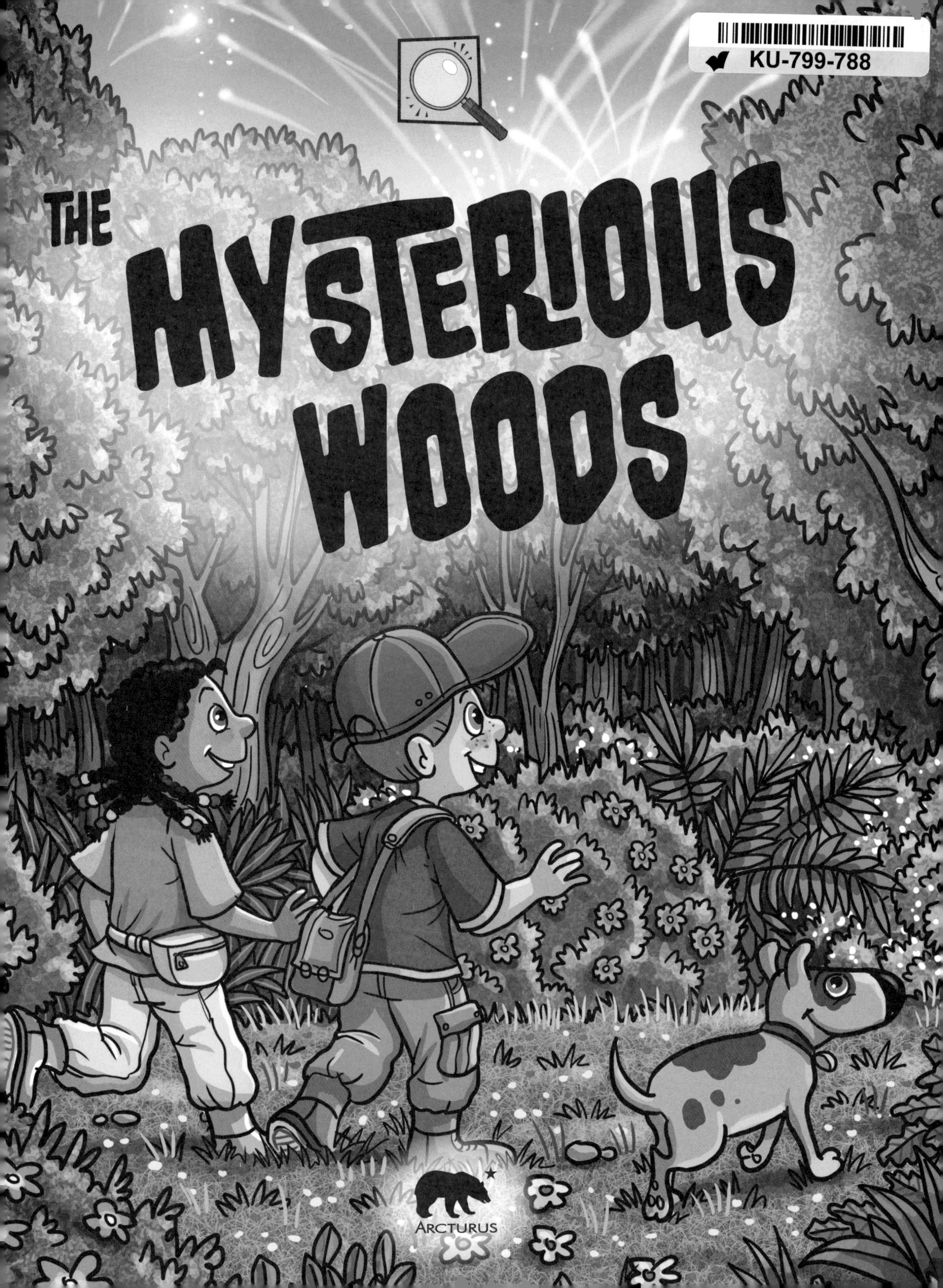
THE
MYSTERIOUS
WOODS
ARCTURUS

This edition published in 2019 by Arcturus Publishing Limited
26/27 Bickels Yard, 151–153 Bermondsey Street,
London SE1 3HA

Written by Gareth Moore
Illustrated by Moreno Chiacchiera
Designed by Paul Oakley, with Emma Randall
Edited by Frances Evans, with Julia Adams

ISBN: 978-1-78950-325-8
CH007004NT
Supplier 33, Date 0219, Print run 8061

Printed in China

an adventure awaits!
Ruby, her best friend Ned, and her dog Mungo are out for a walk in the woods. They are busy admiring the pretty flowers when all of a sudden they hear a loud sneeze, and see sparks shooting into the sky like fireworks. Pen and paper at the ready—it looks like the gang may be about to begin an adventure!
What's that?
Arf?

Which Way?
"My granddad once told me that these woods are enchanted," says Ruby. They want to investigate. Will this signpost give them a clue as to which way to go?
This sign must be magical!
If you really concentrate, the symbols change!
A B C D E F G H I J K L M
N O P Q R S T U V W X Y Z

Muddy Clues

The children spot an information board showing them how to recognize an animal from its footprint. There are certainly plenty of footprints in the mud here. Can you see which animals have been here? What has Mungo spotted?

Magical Pointers
The children hear another sneeze, and see more sparks shooting into the air. They must be close to the magic! Mungo has spotted something interesting again. What is it?
Granddad said that magical things always look a little different.
There's something different about one of these bushes.

Follow the Trail

Ned, Ruby, and Mungo find a path behind the bush. It branches into several different routes. "Look," says Ruby. "Weird patches of burned grass! Let's search them all for clues."

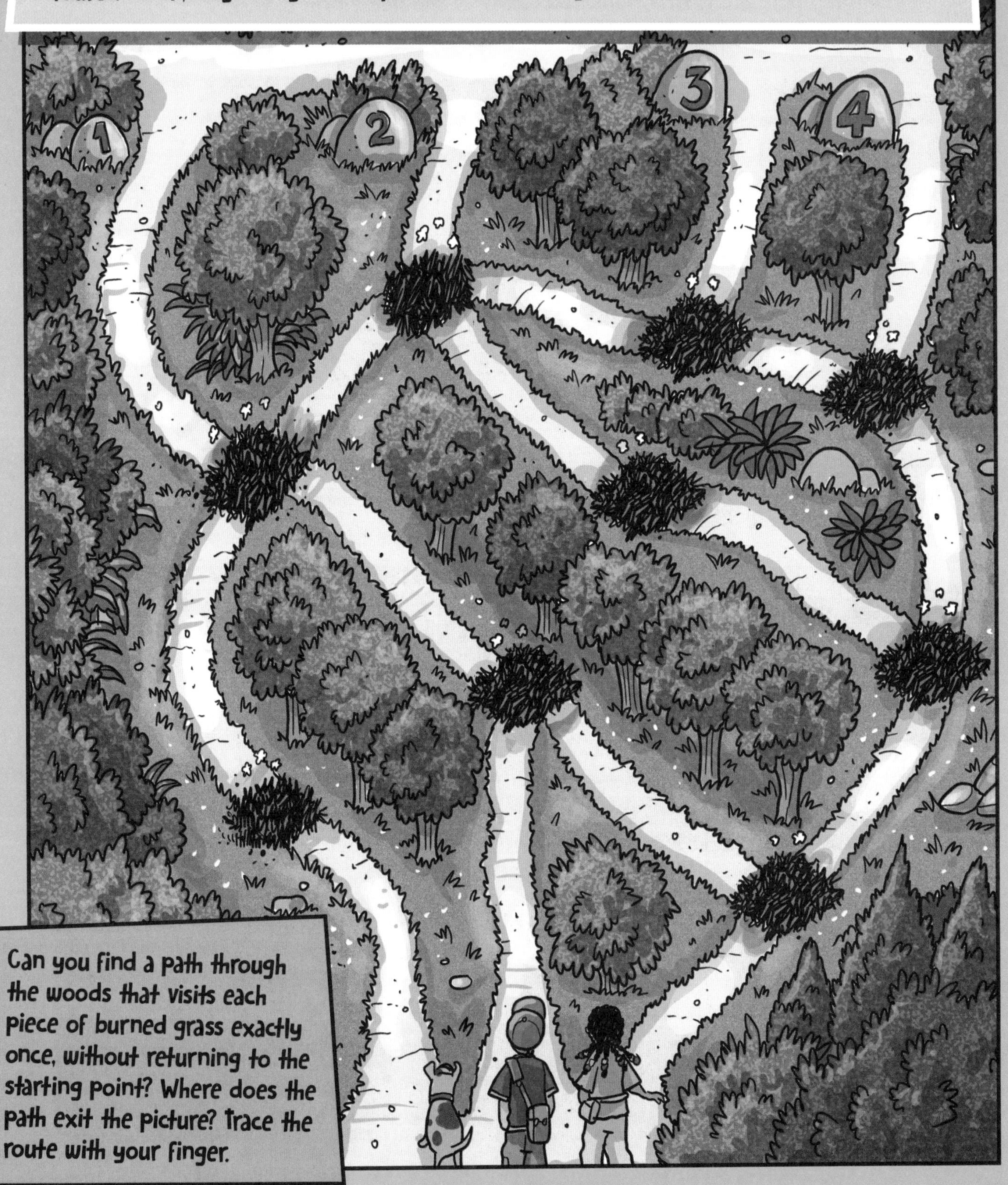

Can you find a path through the woods that visits each piece of burned grass exactly once, without returning to the starting point? Where does the path exit the picture? Trace the route with your finger.

The Mysterious Map

Ned discovers a notebook in one of the patches of burned grass. They walk a little farther, and Ned gives a shout. "Look! There's a map of this clearing in the notebook!" There are instructions, too. "Start at the bee. North 6, West 2, South 4, East 8, South 2, West 2." Where do the kids end up?

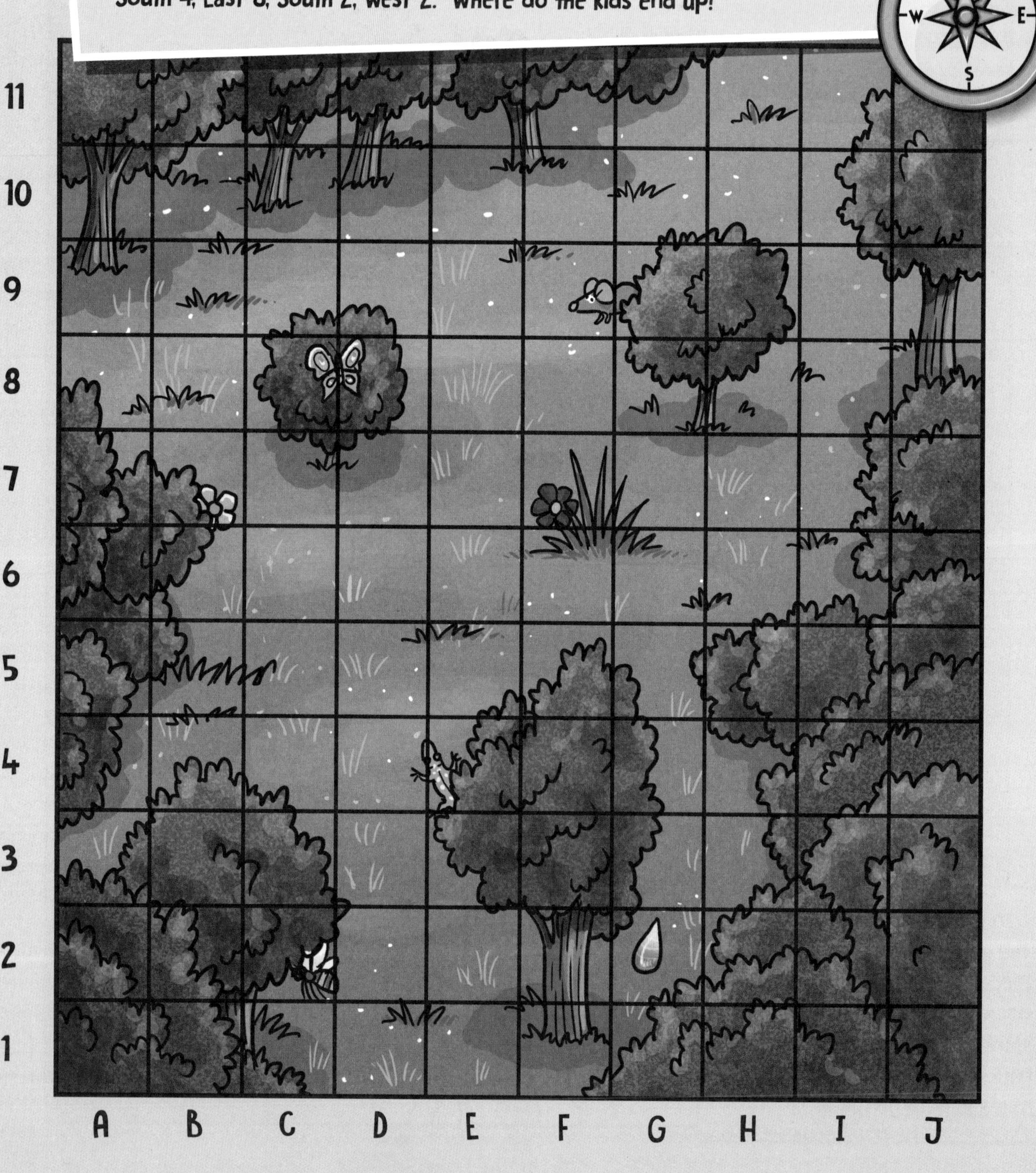

Look in the Book
They find a pink scale lying in the grass. Ned picks it up. "I think the scale wants us to go this way," he says, surprised. "Wait!" says Ruby, "We need to know what creature we're dealing with. I think there might be a clue in the notebook."
Does it leave footprints?
YES
NO
Wood Elf
Does it burn things?
YES
NO
Does it have four legs?
Does it have scales?
YES
NO
Pegasus
Does it wear green?
YES
NO
Phoenix
Does it make sparks?
YES
NO
Leprechaun
Gnome
YES
NO
Dragon
Salamander

Taking Flight

It IS a dragon, and he seems to be in trouble. Can you understand his magic language?

"Whenever I sneeze, I cast a spell!" says the dragon. "My last sneeze must have made these flowers heavy." In what order should you take them away to free him?

Muddled Story

"My name is Snuffles," says the dragon. He starts explaining how he became trapped, but he sneezes again, and his words are magically rearranged. Can you understand him? Use your pen and paper to work out what he is trying to say.

love picking flowers, especially

I'm a garden dragon! I just

the tall ones. However, the pollen makes

are magical!

me sneeze, and dragon sneezes

All Change!

Snuffles the dragon seems very taken with Ned's hat. As the children talk to him, he sneezes again. There is a flash of light, and suddenly the hat is on the dragon's head! There are five other differences, too. Can you see them? Write them down on your piece of paper.

Taking Flight
Before Ned can say anything, Snuffles flies off to the top of a tree ... taking the hat with him! "Follow me! I'll show you the way to the Dragon town." Can you find a way to reach him?
Ned, look, he still has your hat!
Lucky these ladders are here!

14
Slide away
The children reach the top of the tree, but Snuffles has disappeared again. He must have gone down one of the slides! Can you work out which one?
ENCHANTED FOREST SLIDE DESTINATIONS
There is only one slide to each destination, so choose carefully!
• Gnome Town slide: Multiple of 3.
• Pixie City slide: Multiple of 4.
• Leprechaun Village slide: Multiple of 5.
• Dragon Town slide: Multiple of 7.
So the slide that has the number 20 doesn't go to Gnome Town.
And slide 18 doesn't go to Leprechaun Village.
49
18
20
16

Dragon's Den
Ned, Ruby, and Mungo jump onto the slide to Dragon town, which seems to travel downward for a very long time. When they eventually reach the end of it, they find themselves in a long corridor with decorated walls. Ruby spots a note on the floor, and picks it up. What does it say?
CLUE:
Look back at page 4 to find the code!

Sleeping Dragons

Ned and Ruby come to a room that is full of sleepy dragons. They tiptoe past very quietly, so as not to disturb them. They need to find the treasure room, quickly, to get Ned's hat back!

What have Ned and Ruby missed?

The Room of Doors

When they leave the sleepy dragon room, the children find four doors. One of these must be the way to the treasure room. The doors all look the same at a glance, but can you spot the one that is different in some way?

Treasure Chest

They picked the right door! This is the treasure room, and there is Snuffles, their dragon friend. He asks them to help him find which treasure chest is his.

Hat Trick

The dragon is very grateful to the children, and agrees to give Ned's hat back—if they can work out which one it is! He shows them his hat collection.

Into the Garden

Snuffles then asks Ruby and Ned if they want to see the most valuable treasure of all. The children say yes, and the dragon leads them out ... into a garden full of flowers! He is a garden dragon, after all.

Ruby and Ned love the shape of the flowerbeds. Can you work out which of the garden maps matches the garden they can see?

Mungo Finds Some Flowers

Mungo wanders over to some huge flowers. Snuffles becomes excited. "Let's pick some as a gift for my parents," he says. Snuffles wants to pick as many as possible, but he wants to make sure his bunch of flowers has an even number of petals in total. What is the maximum number of flowers he can give them?

Meet the Parents
"Look," says Snuffles, "It's my parents!" They are at the other end of a path. Ned and Ruby are eager to meet them, but Snuffles warns them to avoid stepping on paving stones that contain a multiple of 3. "The number 3 is unlucky to dragons!" Can you find a route from him to his parents? Trace it with your finger.
3
6
4
62
5
2
1
9
7
54
15
63
9
57
21
32
18
42
48
12
43
51
11
7
33
69
6

Which Watering Can?

Snuffles' parents love the flowers he picked for them, and can't wait to plant some more. However, Snuffles' dad has lost his magical watering can, which helps the flowers to grow extra large! Can you help him to find it?

a Handful of Jewels!

The dragons are very happy with how helpful the children have been. Snuffles' dad holds out a paw with some precious jewels in it. He tells Ned that he can have the one that is made up of six triangles, but which one is it?

Gem-tastic

Now it is Ruby's turn. She picks the jewel that was not shown to Ned. Can you work out which it is?

Taking Flight
Snuffles' dad says he will fly the children home, but first he wants them to solve a riddle. "Which of these patterns can be found on my blanket?"
1
2
3
4

Trading Gifts

It's time to go. Ned gives his hat to Snuffles. "Perhaps it will help with all the sneezing." In exchange, the dragon gives them something from the treasure room: an object that all of the treasure chests contained. What is it?

Looking Down

Ned and Ruby have a great view of the countryside from the back of the dragon. They just have to decide where to land.

CLUE:
What is Ned holding?

Dragon Departure
Ruby and Ned have had an amazing adventure. They particularly enjoyed flying back at the end! How many animals capable of flying can you spot in this picture?
I wish I could fly!

Answers

Page 4

Page 5 All of the animals on the signpost have left footprints. Here are some of them:

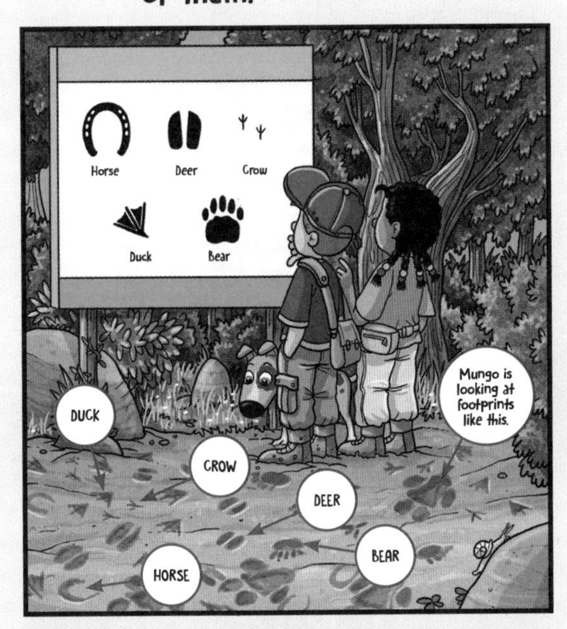

Page 6 The flowers have fewer petals.

Page 7

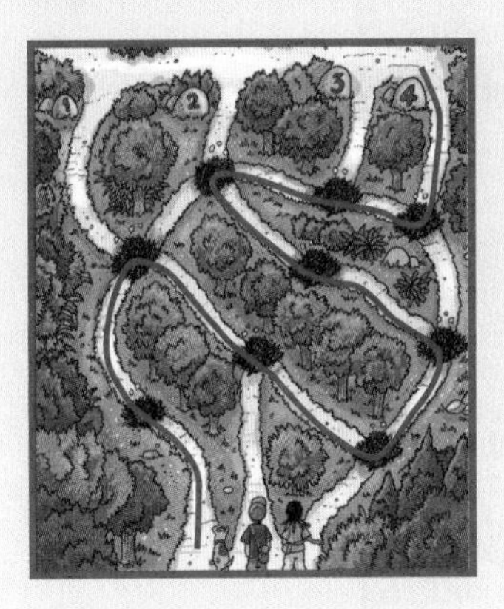

Page 8 They end up at G2.

Page 9 The creature is a dragon.

Page 10 (Top) The message says: "The flowers are magically heavy!"

Page 10 (Bottom) Remove the flowers in this order: orange, red or blue, yellow, purple, pink.

Page 11 The dragon says:
"I'm a garden dragon! I just love picking flowers, especially the tall ones. However, the pollen makes me sneeze, and dragon sneezes are magical!"

Page 12

Page 13

Page 14 Slide 18 goes to Gnome town.
Slide 16 goes to Pixie City.
Slide 20 goes to Leprechaun Village
Slide 49 goes to Dragon town.

Page 15 The message reads:
MEET YOU IN THE TREASURE ROOM, FRIENDS

Page 16 Ned and Ruby have not spotted that their friend Snuffles is hiding with the other dragons.

Page 17

Page 18

Page 19

Page 20 The correct map is this one:

B

Page 21 Snuffles can give all six flowers to his parents. They all have five petals, and 6 flowers x 5 petals is 30, which is an even number of petals.

Page 22

Page 23

Page 24

Page 25 The answer is 2.

Page 26 Snuffles' gift to the children is a ruby ring.

Page 27

Page 28

Glossary

enchanted When someone or something is under a spell.

leprechaun In Irish folk tales, a small, mischievous fairy.

multiple A multiple of four is a number that can be divided by four exactly.

pollen A fine, yellow, powdery substance that can be found in flowers.

Further Information

Books:

Dreidemy, Joelle. *The Great Big Search and Find Book.* London, UK: QED Publishing, 2017.

Tyler, Jenny. *Puzzle Adventure Omnibus, Volume 1* (Usborne Puzzle Adventure). London, UK: Usborne Publishing, 2007.

Usborne Publishing. *99 Maths Puzzles.* London, UK: Usborne Publishing, 2015.

Websites:

https://www.bbc.co.uk/cbbc/joinin/bp-can-you-find-it-puzzles
Can you solve these mind-bending picture puzzles?

https://www.bbc.co.uk/cbbc/curations/bp-radzi-riddles-and-quizzes
Visit this BBC site every Monday to solve new puzzles and find out the answers to the previous week's ones.

Index